ENGLISH

Skills Book

2a

ACTIVITIES FOR GROUP WORK

Contents

How to use this book

 read or look

 write or draw

 share or discuss

Clothes words

 Look.

1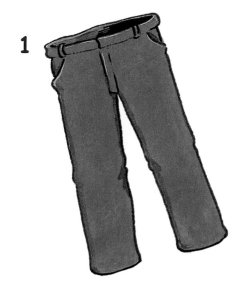

2

3

4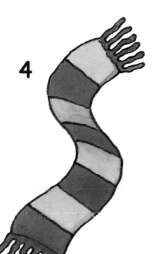

5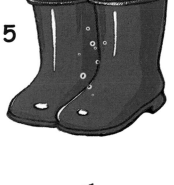

6

 Write the words.

3

New words ◆◆
Skill: Identifying and writing new words.
Instructions: Look carefully at the picture and write the six 'clothes' words.
If time, add more 'clothes' words to the list.

Building words

1. Read the start of this story.

The Building Site

It is early morning. The building site is quiet. Nothing disturbs Old Sam and his dog Tinker. The works van arrives.

"Let's have no dawdling about now, lads," says J K Biggs, the foreman, to his men.

Aaah! Oooh! Old Sam and Tinker stretch and yawn.

Scrunch! Scrape! The digger starts to dig.

Rumble! Slurp! The cement truck mixes and pours.

"This way a bit!" Eddie shouts to the crane driver.

2. Write words from the story.

vehicles

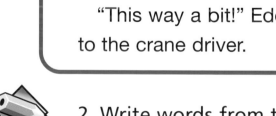

noises

New words ◆◆◆

Skill: Identifying new words from reading.
Instructions: Read the story carefully and then write lists of words that describe vehicles and noises. If time, add more words to each list.

Making words

Join the word parts to make words.

un

dis

appear

help

play

pack

fair

ful

cross

slow

wonder

s

ly

ing

ed

Using word-level skills ◆◆
Skill: Making words from word parts.
Instructions: Write new words using the word parts in the thought bubbles. Make short words and long words.

Sounds funny

1. Read the questions.

2. Write **yes** or **no**.

- Do you eat green peas with your knees?

- Is it raining snails and whales?

- Can you glue a flute to your new boot?

3. Now write some silly questions of your own.

queen bee sea

rain crane train

blue moon June

Long vowel phonemes ◆◆

Skill: Spelling words with long vowel phonemes *ee, ai, oo*
Instructions: Read the funny questions and write *yes* or *no* for each of them.
Then write new questions using some or all of the words in the thought bubbles.

Spelling errors

1. Read this story. It has lots of errors!

Wunce upon a time thare was a little girl called Goldilocks. She went for a work in the woods. She saw a little house. The dore wus open. She pooshed the door and went inside.

"I wonder who livs heer?" she sed.

On the table she sor three bowls of porridge. She was feeling vere hungry. So she ate sum of the porridge in the big bowl. But it wus too hot!

2. Write the correct words.

Common spellings ◆◆◆

Skill: Identifying and correcting mis-spelt high-frequency words.
Instructions: Read the beginning of *Goldilocks and the Three Bears* and identify all the spelling errors.
Write the words correctly – either in a list, or rewrite the story.

Sweet words

Look.

Orange chew

Sherbert lemon

Chocolate coin

Cola cube

Fruit bar

 What will you buy?

2 cola cubes

Word endings ◆

Skill: Adding *s* to make plural words
Instructions: Look at the range of sweets and then write a 'shopping list' for more than one of each sweet.
Add *s* each time to make the plural word. If time, add more plural sweet words to the list.

Sorting words

1. Read the words.

played

climbed

jumping

wanted

reading

jumped

kicked

called

growing

throwing

playing

climbing

2. Write two lists:

ed	ing
played	jumping

Word endings ◆◆
Skill: Identifying and writing words with *ed* and *ing* endings.
Instructions: Find the words with *ed* and *ing* endings and write them in two separate lists headed *ed* and *ing*.
If time, think of more words to add to each list, using the picture for ideas.

Sounds the same

 Read these sentences. Some words are mixed up!

1. I need two buy to new wheels for my bike.

2. Come over hear, please. I can't here you.

3. Wear is my helmet? I must where it every day.

4. Won of my friends one a bike at a fair.

 Write the sentences with the right words.

Homophones ◆◆◆
Skill: Identifying mixed-up words that sound the same.
Instructions: Read the sentences, find the mixed-up words, then rewrite the sentences correctly.

Changing rhymes

1. Read the nursery rhymes.

Humpty Dumpty sat on a wall,
Humpty Dumpty had a great fall.
All the King's horses
And all the King's men
Couldn't put Humpty together again.

Jack and Jill
Went up the hill
To fetch a pail of water.
Jack fell down
And broke his crown
And Jill came tumbling after.

2. Change one word in each line to make new nursery rhymes.

Reading for meaning ◆◆

Skill: Replacing words in context to demonstrate understanding.
Instructions: Change one word in each line of each nursery rhyme, to make new verses.
If time, draw pictures for the new nursery rhymes.

Understanding a story

 Read the story of Pocahontas in the Big Book.

Answer these questions.

1. Where did Pocahontas live?

2. What was the name of Pocahontas's father?

3. How did Pocahontas get her name?
   a. She was the daughter of Powhatan.
   b. She played a lot.
   c. Her mother liked the name.

4. Find two words about what sort of person Powhatan was.

Reading for meaning ◆◆◆
Skill: Basic comprehension questions to test understanding.
Instructions: Reread the story of Pocahontas in the Big Book, then read the questions carefully and answer them.

Using linking words

1. Choose a picture.

2. Write about what to do.
   Use these words to help you.

first

then

before

while

next

after

finally

Linking words ◆◆◆

Skill: Using words and phrases that link sentences.
Instructions: Choose one of the pictures of an everyday activity and write a short explanation of it, using the linking words provided.

Using capitals

1. Read the voice bubbles.

2. Rewrite the voice bubbles using capital letters.

Capital letters ◆◆◆

Skill: Using capital letters for sentences, names and emphasis.
Instructions: Rewrite the voice bubbles for each picture, with capital letters for emphasis.
Make up speech for final voice bubble.

Family tree

 1. This family tree shows the people in Sam's family.

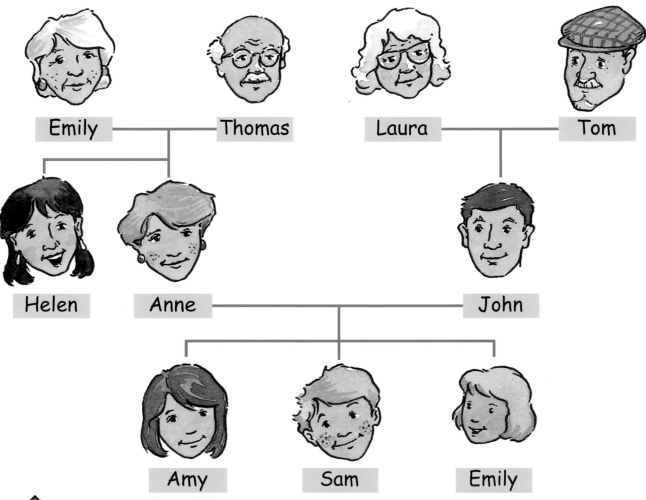

Emily — Thomas   Laura — Tom

Helen   Anne — John

Amy   Sam   Emily

 2. Answer these questions.

- What is Sam's mother called?
- How many sisters does Sam have?
- What is Tom's wife called?
- Who are Sam's grandmothers?

15

Organisation ◆◆
Skill: Using simple organisational devices.
Instructions: Look carefully at the family tree and use the information to answer the questions.
(If time, think of some questions about the tree to ask a friend.)

A letter to Father Christmas

  Read the letter in the Big Book.
Answer the questions.

1. Why did Charlotte write a letter?

2. Who is Ben?
   a. Charlotte's brother
   b. Charlotte's cat
   c. Charlotte's Grandad

3. Where will Charlotte be on Christmas Eve?

4. Who will be in Charlotte's room on Christmas Eve?
   a. Mummy and Daddy
   b. Grandma and Grandad
   c. Charlotte and Ben

Exploring stories ◆◆
Skill: Answering reading comprehension questions.
Instructions: Reread the letter in the Big Book and then answer the questions about it.

Jack's story

 Look.

  Tell the story.

Exploring stories ◆

Skill: Structuring a sequence of events.
Instructions: Use language of time (e.g. *first, then, next, after, finally*) to retell the story of *Jack and the Beanstalk*, using the pictures as prompts. The story could be told orally, or in writing.

Lost and found

 1. Look at this picture from the story.

Dad was nowhere to be seen.

 2. Has this ever happened to you?

 3. Tell your story.

 I remember when

Story themes ◆◆

Skill: Linking story themes to own experiences.
Instructions: Look at the picture from the story in the Big Book. Think about when you have been lost or separated from the person looking after you. Tell the story (either orally or in writing).

The accident

1. Read this story.

Ali had a brand new bike. He rode it down to the park, then he rode it along the path. He got faster and faster.

"Slow down," said Mum, "I can't keep up with you."

Ali rode faster and faster. "Whee! This is fun!" he thought.

Suddenly, his wheel hit a stone and he swerved on to the grass verge. He went over the handle bars and landed in a heap. His knee was cut.

Mum came running up. She was cross. "Ali! Now look what's happened. You were going too fast!"

Mum took Ali and his bike home. There, she bandaged his leg. Then she hugged Ali. Ali felt as if he was about to cry. "Sorry Mum," he whispered. "I won't do that again."

 2. Have you ever had an accident?

 3. Write a story about your accident.

Remember:
- *the beginning* – set the scene
- *the middle* – the accident
- *the ending* – what happens afterwards

Story themes ◆◆◆

Skill: Using story structure to write about own experience in similar form.
Instructions: Read the story about Ali's accident. Think about an accident that you have had (or perhaps a friend), then write a story about it.

Tongue twisters

1. Read this tongue-twister.

Yellow butter purple jelly red jam black bread
Spread it thick
Say it quick

Yellow butter purple jelly red jam black bread
Spread it thicker
Say it quicker

Yellow butter purple jelly red jam black bread
Now repeat it
While you eat it

Yellow butter purple jelly red jam black bread
Don't talk
With your mouth full!

Mary Ann Hoberman

2. What are your favourite foods and drinks?

3. Write and draw your own food tongue twister.

Exploring poems ◆◆
Skill: Exploring word combinations in poems.
Instruction: Think about favourite foods and drinks, using the poem and pictures for ideas.
Write a tongue-twister poem.

Making cakes

 Read these instructions.

How to make Krispie cakes

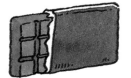 **What you need**

50g chocolate   50g Rice Krispies   12 paper cases   A mixing bowl and a spoon

 **What you do**

1. Wash your hands and put on an apron.

2. Break the chocolate into pieces and put into the bowl.

3. Melt the chocolate in a microwave oven for 30 seconds. (Ask an adult to help.)

4. Mix the chocolate and Rice Krispies.

5. Spoon the mixture into 12 paper cases.

6. Put into the fridge to set.

Answer these questions.

1. What do you need to do before you start cooking?

2. How much chocolate do you need?

3. When do you add the Rice Krispies?
  a. At the beginning
  b. After the chocolate has melted
  c. After they have been in the fridge
  d. After 30 seconds

4. How long do you melt the chocolate for?

5. When are the Krispie cakes ready to eat?

Instructions ◆◆
Skill: Reading and understanding instructions.
Instructions: Read the instructions carefully and answer the questions.

Picture puzzle

 Look.

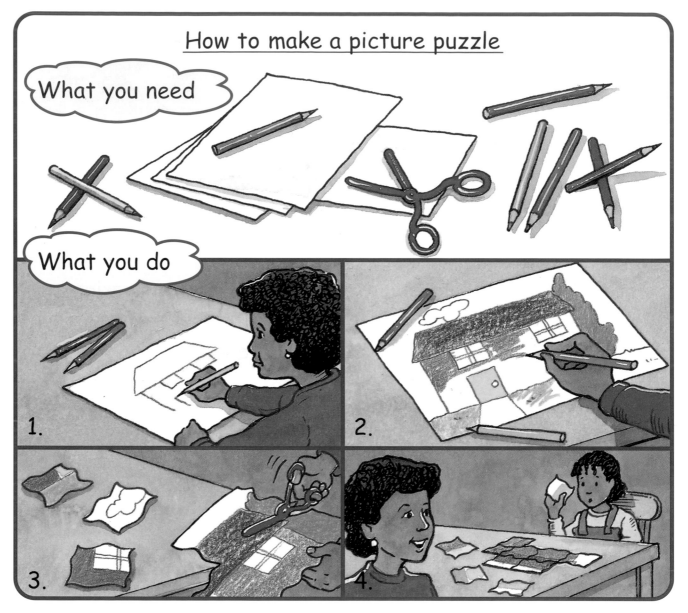

 Write the instructions.

Instructions ◆
Skill: Writing simple instructions.
Instructions: Look at the pictures and write a set of simple instructions to go with them.